Be part of the

Dalmatian 🐾 Press
Puppy Pack!™

Your pictures and ideas could be **spotted** on our new books!

W9-CAV-906

✂ CUT ALONG DOTTED LINES

Dear Dalmatian Press,

my puppy is so cute. It eats my shoes and sneakers. my puppy sleeps in my bed, And sometimes sleeps in her own bed. My puppy is little.

Your Friend, Rory

WRITE YOUR NAME HERE   WRITE YOUR AGE

WHERE DID YOU BUY THIS BOOK?
15510 Baby Animals FBTC

PHONE NUMBER: (In case your letter or picture is picked!)

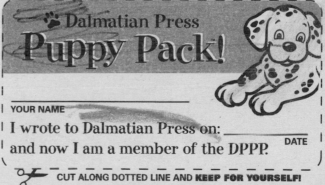

Dalmatian Press
Puppy Pack!™

YOUR NAME

I wrote to Dalmatian Press on: _____
and now I am a member of the DPPP.   DATE

✂ CUT ALONG DOTTED LINE AND **KEEP FOR YOURSELF!**

Here is how to join the Puppy Pack!

1. **ASK** a grown-up to help you **CUT** out the **LETTER** on the first page.

2. **WRITE** and **TELL** us what you...
- like about our coloring books.
- want us to make a coloring book about.
- would change about our books.

3. **ASK** a grown-up for an **ENVELOPE** and a **STAMP**. Be sure to fill out the envelope like **THIS:**

Your name and address

STAMP

Dalmatian Press
P.O. Box 682068
Franklin, TN 37068-2068

4. **NOW,** put your letter and a **PICTURE** you have colored in a **MAILBOX.**

Your name
address

STAMP

Dalmatian Press
P.O. Box 682068
Franklin, TN 37068-2068

5. **WHO** knows? Maybe your **PICTURE** and **IDEAS** will be *spotted* on the next **DALMATIAN** Press book!

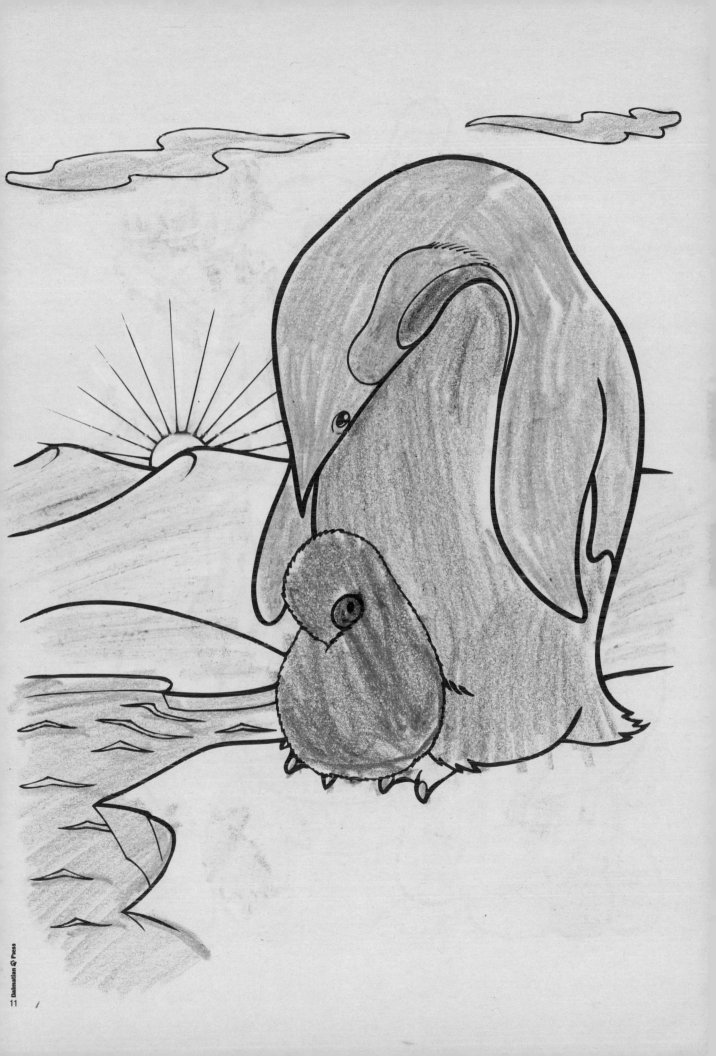

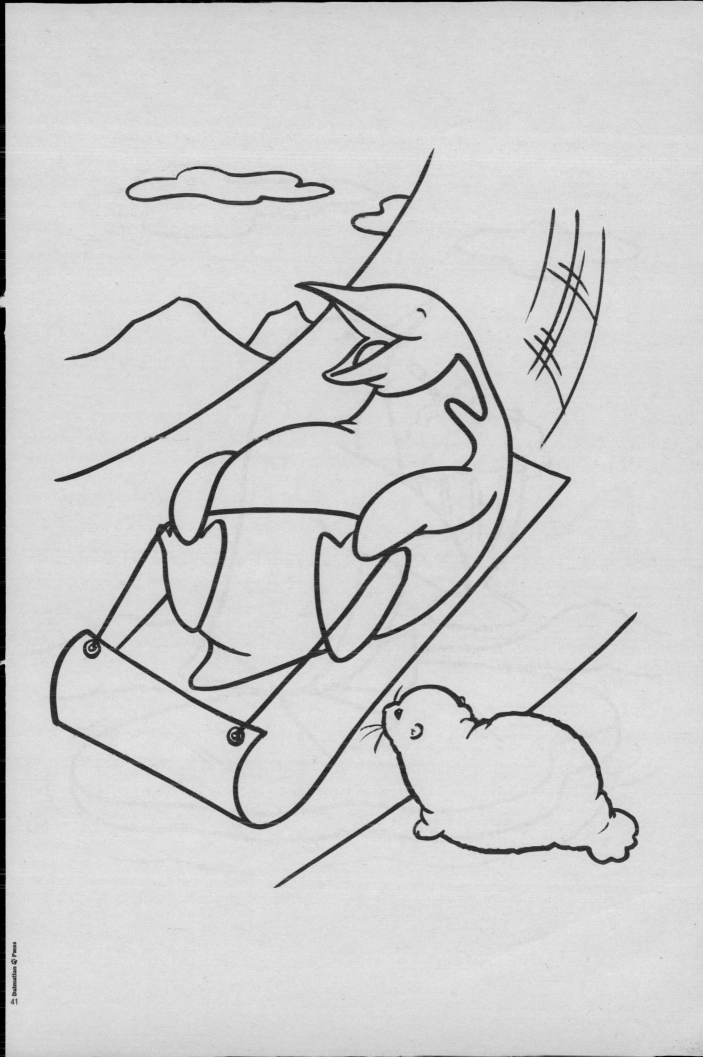